Who Goes Moo?

This book belongs to:

....

Down on the farm
Early one morning,

Tractor Ted wakes
Stretching and yawning.

Midge has a problem...
What can it be?

"I need to find milk
For Farmer Tom's tea."

Tractor Ted smiles...
 And gives Midge a clue,
"Milk comes from an animal.
 One that says **moo**!"

Midge finds the chickens.
What noise will she hear?

Cluck, **cluck** they go,
Not **moo** - that's clear.

Could it be horses
munching their hay?

"No," Tractor Ted says,
"They all say **neigh**."

"Oh no," says Midge,
"What can I do?
How will I find
The ones who say
moo?"

Is it the pigs
        Asleep in their sty?

They go **oink**, **oink**,
So Midge passes by.

On to the dairy...
Who will Midge meet?

Look! Lots of cows
In a row nice and neat.

"**Moo, moo,**"
say the cows.

Midge barks
with delight.

It's the cows who give milk,
Tractor Ted was right!

TED 1

Midge thanks Tractor Ted
  For the helpful **moo** clue,
But she knows there is still
One job left to do…

To see Farmer Tom
And let him know who
Gave him milk for his tea.
It was the cows who say
MOO!

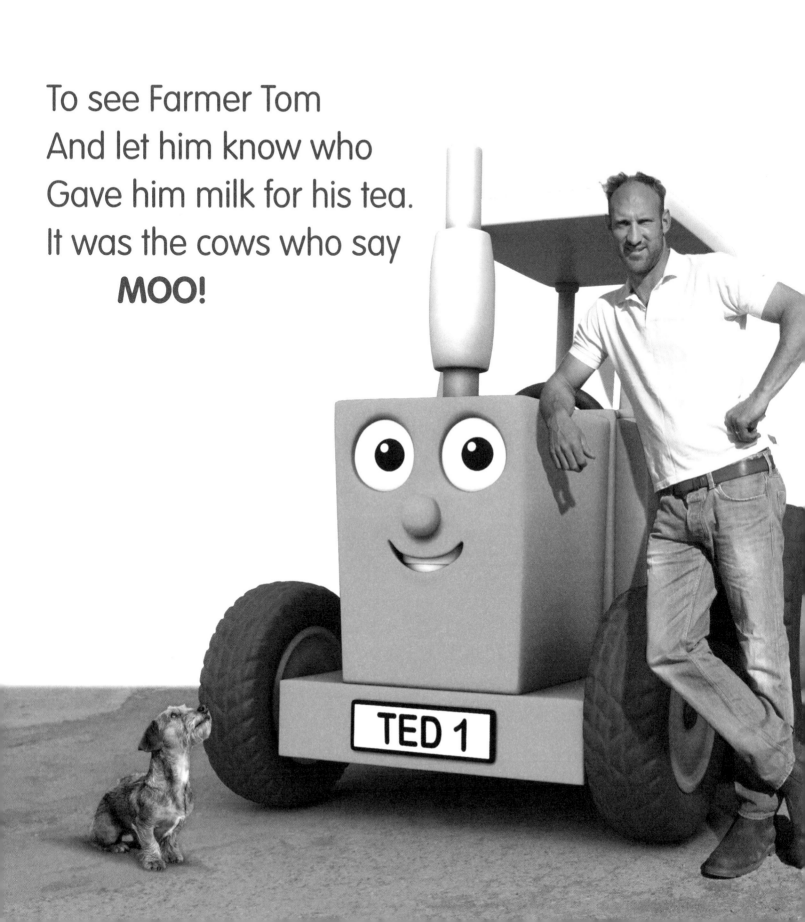